DEAR CHUCK

A one-act dramedy by
Jonathan Dorf

Best wishes,

Jonathan Dorf

www.youthplays.com
info@youthplays.com
424-703-5315

COPYRIGHT RULES TO REMEMBER

CAST OF CHARACTERS

Dear Chuck has a flexible cast. To perform it effectively requires at least 8 performers, but it could use 30 or more. Many roles are gender flexible—just update the pronouns as necessary.

LIST OF SCENES

Overture: The Search for Chuck

The Dance

Chuck Interlude #1

Supposed To

Chuck Interlude #2: Dear Chuck

The Social Network

Chuck Interlude #3

The Menu

Chuck Interlude #4

Helicopter

Chuck Interlude #5

Three Rows*

Zero Tolerance

Chuck Interlude #6

Adventures in Babysitting

Chuck Interlude #7

Babel, or A Cyber Symphony

Chuck Interlude #8: Dear Chuck Reprise

Finale: The Coming of Chuck

*Bran and Bananas, located at the end of the script, may be performed in place of Three Rows.

NOTES

It is possible to condense the number of actors in Overture: The Search for Chuck and Finale: The Coming of Chuck. The cast in the script is based on the size of the Choate cast, which was 31, and it is left to the director to reassign the lines as necessary and appropriate. The actors should use their own names, rather than the names in the script. It's possible that the Girl 22 monologue in Overture: The Search for Chuck could be broken up among several cast members after Girl 22 does the opening paragraph. The same is true of the letter in Chuck Interlude #8. It is possible to break up Chuck Interlude #2, but my inclination would be to give that to a single performer.

Occasionally, alternate text will appear in [brackets].

ACKNOWLEDGMENTS

The following statement should be included in any program: "*Dear Chuck* was originally commissioned and developed by the Choate Rosemary Hall Summer Arts Conservatory."

The play was later revised, going through developmental readings with the assistance of director Jonathan Muñoz-Proulx. Thanks to Nick Podany for helping me test out Bran and Bananas.

Chuck Interlude #2: Dear Chuck is adapted by permission from a journal entry by Daniel Sobol.

OVERTURE: THE SEARCH FOR CHUCK

(A dark stage. Enter GIRL 1.)

GIRL 1: Mom? *(Pause.)* Dad? *(Pause.)* Demon spawn? *(Pause.)* Chuck? *(Pause.)* If you come out, I won't tell Mom and Dad how you put paint chips in the salad! Chuck?!

(Enter GIRL 2.)

GIRL 2: Who's Chuck?

GIRL 1: Who are you?

(Enter GIRL 3.)

GIRL 3: I asked you first.

GIRL 1 & GIRL 2: No you didn't.

(Enter BOY 1.)

BOY 1: Will you chicks stop screaming?

GIRLS: Chicks?

BOY 1: Girls. Sorry.

(Enter GIRL 4.)

GIRL 1: I'm not a girl.

(Enter GIRL 5.)

GIRL 4: I'm a woman.

(Enter GIRL 6 carrying a sign that says "Feed the Hungry.")

GIRL 5: A young woman.

GIRL 6: Woman. Young woman. Girl. Chick. We ought to be out saving the rain forest.

(She sees that her sign is wrong and flips it. Enter BOY 2.)

Saving the rain forest.

(Girl 6's sign now reads, "Save the Whales.")

And the whales.

(Enter GIRL 7.)

BOY 2: Do you know how many trees you're killing?

(Enter BOY 3 and GIRL 8.)

GIRL 7: Does anybody know how to get out of here?

BOY 3: Where's here?

GIRL 8: Has anybody seen Chuck?

(Enter GIRL 9.)

GIRL 1: You know Chuck?

GIRL 8: He's my demon spawn little brother.

GIRL 1 & GIRL 9: No, he's *my* demon spawn little brother.

GIRL 10: Maybe he got out.

BOY 4: There's no doors.

BOY 5: *(Pointing at different groups of kids:)* You three look over there. And you — sign girl — you go look —

GIRL 11: Who said you were the boss?

BOY 5: I'm a man.

GIRL 12: You're short.

BOY 5: I'm sixteen. I've got my driver's license.

GIRL 13: Do you have a car?

GIRL 14: *(Beat.)* You're a boy.

(Pause. Actors should enter until the entire cast is onstage.)

I like boys.

(She kisses him on the lips.)

But you're not in charge. *(Pause.)* You three look over there. Sign girl—you go look over there. Boys, come with me.

(All on stage begin looking for exits to no avail.)

BOY 6: We should sound off.

GIRL 15: Sound off?

BOY 6: Say your name and if you found something.

GIRL 15: Chuck!

GIRL 16: Your name's not Chuck.

GIRL 17: Everyone should say their name.

GIRL 18: What are we looking for again?

GIRL 19: A door!

BOY 7: Or a window. We could climb out a window.

GIRL 20: I'm not climbing out a window.

GIRL 21: I thought we were saying our names. I'll start. My name is...

(Each member of the cast should sound off by saying his or her name. This should go as quickly as possible.)

BOY 8: Has anyone seen Chuck?

BOY 9: *(Points one way:)* I bet he's over there. *(Points in the opposite direction, like the Scarecrow in* The Wizard of Oz:*)* Or over there. Or—

GIRL 22: Nobody's seen Chuck. Not in a while. Most of you don't even remember what he looks like. Some of you think you do, but you don't. Chuck is a metaphor. He's that elusive moment of knowing who you are, and when you're a teenager, most of the time you're pretty Chuck-free. *(Beat.)* When you're a little kid, you've got your Chuck squared away. Your job is to make nice in the sandbox, to eat what they give you and try to get most of it in the toilet, to scream for your way every now and again, do your coloring homework and to hold your mom or dad's hand when you're crossing the street and at other strategic moments. *(Beat.)* When you get much older, you'll have had time to try out different Chucks and figure out which one is for you. Maybe it's the family Chuck or the career Chuck or a pet Lab named Chuck or all or none of the above. *(Beat.)* But in between kid Chuck and grown-up Chuck, there's a whole lot of out-of-focus Chuck and absent Chuck, followed by drive-by Chuckings and frantic Chuck chases and arriving at a Chuck stop only to find out he just left. And people will tell you that you didn't really see Chuck for that second you thought you did, and you'll start to ask yourself that and is this new Chuck worth the trouble and wouldn't it just be easier to sit back down in the sandbox? *(Beat.)* Like it or not, after a while we get too big for the sandbox, and like it or not, Chuck doesn't come out to play anymore. So we have to find him. Like it or not, it's just something we do. *(To the cast:)* I hear that Chuck is just on the other side of the door — if we can find one.

BOY 1: *(Finds the stage exit:)* Door!

(A mass exit begins. Girl 1 rushes past Boy 1.)

GIRL 1: Chuck?!

GIRL 8: Chuck's there?

BOY 8: Chuck!

THE DANCE

(The "back to school" dance, with signage to say so. A BOY and a GIRL dance a slow dance to whatever is the song of the moment. Around them, other BOYS and GIRLS may do likewise.)

BOY: Your hair smells really great.

(The rest of the scene plays like a typical scene at a school dance, with the couple getting closer and closer. They are not, however, actually saying these things out loud until the Girl's final line.)

GIRL: I have an eight-page paper due Monday on *Wuthering Heights* and I can't find the movie anywhere.

BOY: Frank Smith is away visiting his dad this weekend, so I told him I'd take his shifts at Burger King. Hate that job.

GIRL: Shelley has a flask of Tequila. She wants me to go to the bathroom with her. I don't really want to, but I don't want her to think I'm a loser.

BOY: The rep from UCLA [feel free to substitute an appropriate school] is gonna' be at school on Tuesday. I always wanted to go there, but I don't even know anything about it.

GIRL: I'm so sick of playing soccer. I swear my mom cares more about it than I do.

BOY: My grandfather's in the hospital again. He's gonna' be fine, but I gotta' go over and pick up his mail.

GIRL: Was the cast list for the play posted yet?

BOY: I probably should talk to my parents more.

GIRL: My little brother actually likes soccer. I feel bad that I haven't gone to any of his games this year.

BOY: When are my feet gonna' stop growing?

GIRL: He keeps asking when am I gonna' come see him play, and I always make up some stupid excuse. Next time he asks...

BOY: I never read for fun anymore. I used to do it all the time.

GIRL: Are all my friends really hooking up?

BOY: I like you a lot, but I don't know how far I'm ready to go yet.

GIRL: *(Beat.)* Thanks. Your hair smells nice too.

(The music crescendos as they dance offstage and the scene ends. Beat. A GIRL runs across the stage. She is CHUCK INTERLUDE #1.)

GIRL: Chuck! Chuck! Stop!

(She stops.)

Did anybody see a guy, kinda' short, kinda' tall? Did anybody see which way he went? *(Pause.)* Chuck, come back!

(She exits on the run.)

SUPPOSED TO

(Two GIRLS in a school corridor.)

GIRL 1: He is so in love with you.

GIRL 2: He doesn't even talk to me.

GIRL 1: He wants to. Look.

(BOY 1 walks by.)

GIRL 2: I don't see it.

GIRL 1: Look again.

(The Boy "rewinds" across the stage to the point of his entrance. He then repeats his walk past the girls in slow motion.)

There.

(The Boy freezes. Girl 1 approaches the Boy so that she can point directly at his slightly open mouth:)

See how his mouth is open a little right here.

GIRL 2: Isn't that just from breathing?

GIRL 1: No—that's talking. Definitely trying to talk. He just needs a little help.

GIRL 2: What kind of help?

(Enter GIRLS 3, 4, 5.)

GIRL 1: You should ask him out.

GIRL 3: He is totally your Mr. Right.

GIRL 4: Do you want to be the only girl in our grade that doesn't have a boyfriend?

GIRL 5: The only girl.

GIRL 4: We all have boyfriends.

GIRL 3: You're supposed to.

GIRL 5: It's a rule.

GIRL 3: You're 16 — not 3.

(Girls 3, 4 and 5 take up positions to watch the rest of the scene as the Boy begins to walk toward the edge of the stage.)

GIRL 1: See that?

(The Boy freezes again.)

GIRL 2: What?

GIRL 1: That look. He's dying to ask you out.

GIRL 2: So why doesn't he?

GIRL 1: Maybe his lips are stuck. His lips are stuck, and they're keeping the rest of his mouth from moving.

GIRL 2: I don't know how to ask him out.

GIRLS 3, 4, 5: You what?

GIRL 1: You'd better think of something. He's not going to wait forever.

GIRL 2: I don't know what to say. What should I say?

GIRL 1: I don't know. Say what *he* said.

(Girl 2 approaches the Boy. Both sculpt their mouths into the exact same silent, half-open pose and freeze in it while Girls 1, 3, 4 and 5 watch their efforts.)

CHUCK INTERLUDE #2: DEAR CHUCK

(Enter an ACTOR of either gender holding pen and paper. The Actor sits and writes.)

ACTOR: *(Reading the letter:)* Dear Chuck,

Nothing's been the same since you left. I know you probably won't ever see this letter, and even if you do, I know it probably won't make you come home. But I wanted to tell you some thoughts I've been thinking, just in case.

(Pause.)

I've been thinking about hair. I've been thinking how there's a moment when hair is neither wet nor dry. I get out of the shower and dry my hair with a towel, and it clings. It clings to my head and it lingers in this unconfident place where it wants to fill out and expand, but instead it remains indescribably moist, vulnerable. I think I am my hair right now.

(Pause.)

I am so ready to grow and take on this new part of my life, this next exploration—but something's holding me back. I want to move on, but what do I want to move on to? My mind is asking new, startling questions of me, and I don't know how to respond.

(Pause.)

I talk constantly of how well I know myself and what I believe, but then I wonder if I only say it so much because I'm trying to convince myself it's true. All the old words I used to describe me and what I'm thinking don't seem to have the same meanings anymore, and I want to use new ones...and I keep coming back to hair.

(*Pause.*)

Chuck, I need you to come back. I know you'd have the answers to all these questions in my head. Please come home.

Love,

(*The Actor should say his or her name here, then seal the letter in an envelope and exit with it.*)

THE SOCIAL NETWORK

(*A CLIPBOARD-CARRYING TEEN sits across from another TEEN clutching an application.*)

CLIPBOARD-CARRYING TEEN: So tell me about your experience.

APPLICANT TEEN: Well, I worked at Cream 'n Stuff for like a year.

CLIPBOARD-CARRYING TEEN: That's...

APPLICANT TEEN: Ice cream. And stuff.

CLIPBOARD-CARRYING TEEN: Stuff like...?

APPLICANT TEEN: We "stuff" your ice cream with anything you want. Chocolate chips, marshmallows, nuts...more ice cream...

CLIPBOARD-CARRYING TEEN: Ah. I get it. (*Beat.*) But you left.

APPLICANT TEEN: My parents—and me—I—we believe that school comes first. After the summer, I left (*As if trying to remember something that's been memorized:*) to focus on my academics. But now that we're past Halloween and I've got school under control, I feel like I'm ready for a job. Baby needs a new pair of shoes, right?

CLIPBOARD-CARRYING TEEN: Baby what?

APPLICANT TEEN: Sorry. Just makin' a joke.

CLIPBOARD-CARRYING TEEN: Don't make jokes.

APPLICANT TEEN: Sorry.

CLIPBOARD-CARRYING TEEN: *(Beat.)* So why Cup 'a Joe?

APPLICANT TEEN: 'Cause after you eat some ice cream, what's better than coffee?

CLIPBOARD-CARRYING TEEN: Didn't I just say no jokes? Otherwise I'm just gonna leave.

APPLICANT TEEN: No — sorry. *(Beat.)* I feel like I can take the same skills I learned at Cream 'n Stuff and use them for this job. Customer service skills, I mean. Not the ice cream scooping.

CLIPBOARD-CARRYING TEEN: *(Making notes on the clipboard:)* Great.

APPLICANT TEEN: Are you really writing notes? *(Beat.)* Sorry.

CLIPBOARD-CARRYING TEEN: So tell me about Facebook [or the social media network of the moment].

APPLICANT TEEN: What?

CLIPBOARD-CARRYING TEEN: The Facebook photo. Or was it Instagram? *(Checking something on the clipboard:)* I think it was both.

APPLICANT TEEN: What are you talking about?

CLIPBOARD-CARRYING TEEN: Anytime somebody applies for a job, we check all their profiles.

APPLICANT TEEN: *(Beat.)* I got hacked.

CLIPBOARD-CARRYING TEEN: It's your photo.

APPLICANT TEEN: Yeah, but nobody was supposed to post it. *(Breaking "character":)* What are you doing?

CLIPBOARD-CARRYING TEEN: That's not the kind of conduct we expect from an employee of Cup 'o Joe.

APPLICANT TEEN: Stop for a second.

CLIPBOARD-CARRYING TEEN: We can't hire someone who —

APPLICANT TEEN: Stop!

CLIPBOARD-CARRYING TEEN: *(Beat.)* They're gonna check.

APPLICANT TEEN: I took it down.

CLIPBOARD-CARRYING TEEN: It might still be archived.

APPLICANT TEEN: You're supposed to be helping me, not...this.

CLIPBOARD-CARRYING TEEN: I *am* helping.

APPLICANT TEEN: *(Beat.)* What am I supposed to do?

CLIPBOARD-CARRYING TEEN: Hope nobody finds it. And don't let anybody take any more pictures of you doin' dumb stuff.

APPLICANT TEEN: Or not do the dumb stuff in the first place.

CLIPBOARD-CARRYING TEEN: Now you're thinkin'.

APPLICANT TEEN: Now I'm boring. Pretty soon I'll be my parents.

CLIPBOARD-CARRYING TEEN: Least they have jobs.

APPLICANT TEEN: Truth.

CHUCK INTERLUDE #3

(An ACTOR of either gender.)

ACTOR: I'm having lunch at school, and there's this new kid. I guess he transferred, 'cause I've never seen him before, it's halfway through the year, and there he is, standing in the middle of the cafeteria with a tray. He looks around — and it's weird, 'cause he's not moving. He's just checkin' it all out with his eyes, and then he starts walkin' toward my table. It's just me, 'cause the rest of my friends are still in the line, and he says, "Can I sit here?" And I'm like whatever, 'cause it's gotta' be tough to be somewhere new and not know where to go.

(Pause.)

He says, "Thanks — my name's Chuck." And he sits. No — not sits. He settles. You know like how there's all that stuff at the bottom of your drink if you don't shake it? It's like that. Only in a good way. Like a blanket. Comfortable. Like he's been there all along. I'm thinking maybe he's gonna' be my new best friend.

(Pause.)

I see the rest of my friends coming, and I turn and tell them to hurry up — "you gotta' meet Chuck." Only when I turn back, he's gone. No Chuck, no tray, even the little spill from the canned peaches is dry. And that feeling, that bottom of the drink feel good feeling, it's gone. Every once in a while if I try really hard, I can make myself remember what it was like to sit next to Chuck, but it's not the same. *(Beat.)* Chuck, if you're out there, if you can hear me, I'm saving you a seat at lunch.

THE MENU

(Four teens, one BOY and three GIRLS, sit at a restaurant. A teen WAITRESS takes their order.)

GIRL 1: And I'll have the grilled cheese.

WAITRESS: Grilled cheese?

GIRL 1: *(Shows her on the menu:)* Yeah. Here.

BOY: I want the grilled cheese too.

WAITRESS: Oh — that's the kids' menu.

GIRL 1: Yeah.

WAITRESS: You need to look at the first three pages.

GIRL 1: But those are all ribs and giant platters.

WAITRESS: We specialize in ribs. They're really good here. The baby backs are my favorite, but pretty much all of them are awesome.

GIRL 1: I don't like ribs.

GIRL 2: I don't eat meat.

WAITRESS: Would you like our snow pea and mushroom salad?

GIRL 2: Why can't we order off the kids' menu?

WAITRESS: It's for kids under 12.

GIRL 1: It's a small portion — right?

WAITRESS: That's why it's for kids under 12.

GIRL 1: So if I want a small portion, why can't I get the grilled cheese?

BOY: Yeah. Why can't we get the grilled cheese?

WAITRESS: Let me ask the kitchen. I'm sure they can make you a grilled cheese.

GIRL 1: The kid-sized one.

WAITRESS: I don't think we can do that—but I'm sure they can make you a regular one.

GIRL 1: But I don't want a regular one.

GIRL 3: Why don't we just split a regular one?

GIRL 1: No—I want the one off the kids' menu.

WAITRESS: I need to ask the manager.

BOY: Can't you just pretend we're under 12?

WAITRESS: You're not under 12.

BOY: I know—but can't you just pretend?

GIRL 3: Maybe just this once? Like a Christmas gift?

GIRL 1: We should be able to get it anytime.

WAITRESS: Let me get the manager.

GIRL 1: Whose side are you on?

WAITRESS: I should get—

BOY: *(To Girl 1:)* Yeah, tell her.

GIRL 1: How old are you?

WAITRESS: Can I get you something to drink first?

GIRL 1: You go to our school—right?

WAITRESS: And I have to pay my car insurance, so can I get you something to drink?

GIRL 1: Do you have a kids' drink menu?

WAITRESS: I'm getting the manager.

    (Girl 1 climbs onto the table.)

GIRL 3: *(Trying not to attract attention:)* Katie, get down!

GIRL 1: I declare the Rib Eye officially occupied.

GIRL 3: Oh my God—my parents are going to kill me.

(The Boy jumps up with Girl 1.)

BOY: Yeah, this place is so occupied.

(The Waitress gives up and exits.)

GIRL 1: Brothers, sisters—we will take back the Rib Eye just like our brothers and sisters took back the kiddie pool at the swim club.

(Girl 3 moves to hide under the table.)

Join us.

BOY: Yeah! Stand on your tables!

GIRL 2: I'm afraid of heights.

GIRL 1: And we will eat no ribs until we have a choice to eat off the kids' menu.

(Girl 2 conquers her fear and slowly joins them on the table.)

BOY: Yeah! Pro-choice!

GIRL 1: Does anybody know "We Shall Overcome"?

*(Transition to **CHUCK INTERLUDE #4**: as the actors exit, enter an ACTOR of either gender whose attire perhaps suggests a chauffeur's uniform holding a sign that says "Chuck." The Actor should be dressed in heavy winter clothes, perhaps a hat, scarf, gloves and a heavy coat. Beat. The Actor removes the gloves and the heavy coat. Beat. The Actor should remove one more layer and the scarf, revealing a windbreaker or other light jacket, and perhaps a baseball cap instead of the heavy hat. The attire should now reflect spring. Beat. The Actor gives up and exits.)*

HELICOPTER

(A college tour. A STUDENT TOUR GUIDE leads a group of STUDENTS and PARENTS, including GIRL 1 and MOTHER 1 and GIRL 2 and MOTHER 2.)

TOUR GUIDE: The university of your choice has more than 200 clubs and athletic teams at the varsity through intramural levels.

GIRL 1: Can you tell us about the —

MOTHER 1: Yes, my daughter has a question.

GIRL 1: *(Dying:)* Mom...

MOTHER 1: Pretend I'm not even here. But I know my daughter is wondering how your admissions office weighs extracurricular activities.

GIRL 1: That is not my —

MOTHER 1: I'm just a fly on the wall.

GUIDE: Well, I just give the tours, but —

MOTHER 1: Not to put you on the spot, but where on a scale of one to ten would you place student council president?

MOTHER 2: Where indeed. My daughter was wondering the exact same thing.

GIRL 2: *(Dying:)* Mom...

MOTHER 2: She was also wondering, on a scale of one to ten, where you would rate president of the mathematics tutoring club.

MOTHER 1: What an incredible coincidence. My daughter was wondering where you'd rate — on a scale of one to ten — president of the combined mathematics and foreign language tutoring club.

MOTHER 2: Did I say the mathematics tutoring club? Of course I meant to say the mathematics tutoring club, but I left out vice-president of the conservation club—

MOTHER 1: And I left out senior vice-president treasurer of the young entrepreneurs club.

MOTHER 2: President of bakers against poverty.

(As the mother vs. mother battle continues in pantomime, the two Girls and the rest of the tour sneak away.)

GIRL 1: *(To the Guide:)* Is it true that they serve ice cream every day?

TOUR GUIDE: Yep. One of our alums gave a hundred mill on the condition that we have ice cream available for lunch and dinner.

GIRL 2: That's so awesome. I hope they have cookies 'n cream.

GIRL 1: I love cookies 'n cream.

GIRL 2: Isn't it just the best?

TOUR GUIDE: Every Wednesday. But do not overlook the banana fudge swirl. Just sayin'.

(They exit. The sound comes back up on the Mothers, who still duel.)

MOTHER 1: President for two years running of the high school fire and rescue auxiliary.

MOTHER 2: Invented the tapered blanket for toddlers.

MOTHER 1: Discovered a new word for the color blue.

MOTHER 2: State basket-weaving champion, junior division.

MOTHER 1: National 18 and under full contact origami champion!

(The Mothers realize they are alone.)

Hmm...

MOTHER 2: *(Pulling out a cell phone:)* Not a problem. I track her phone.

MOTHER 1: *(Waving her off:)* She'll be back. They think they're all independent, but they always come crawling back, crawling back for their social security number or someone to proofread their essays or pay for another application, and of course for my signature, my all-important signature, because nothing happens in my daughter's life without my signature. Not one thing. So we'll just sit right here and wait.

MOTHER 2: You said it, sister mother. We'll just sit right here, for as long as it takes.

> *(Beat. Lights dim on them, waiting. As the lights fade to black, a RECORDED VOICEMAIL GREETING plays:* **CHUCK INTERLUDE #5.***)*

VOICEMAIL GREETING: You have reached Chuck's voicemail. Chuck isn't here right now. He's out there. This isn't his voice. That would be too easy. At the beep, you know what to do. Or maybe you're calling because you don't.

> *(The sound of a voicemail beep, or the actor who voices the greeting could simply say "beep.")*

THREE ROWS

> *(After a funeral. An ACTOR of either gender. BRAN AND BANANAS, at the end of the script, may be substituted for this monologue depending on the needs of your production.)*

ACTOR: They didn't have the funeral 'til a week after, so you'd think it wouldn't be that bad, 'cause people have time to get over it a little, and the casket was closed, so it's not like you see him lying there. He probably wouldn't look horrible—I don't know, maybe his neck would be a little funky-looking from the rope, but it's not like he stuck a gun in his mouth. Not like his face is missing.

(*Pause.*)

And almost our entire grade is there, and some of the kids that knew him from other grades, and all the teachers and some of the parents are there. My mom says she's not sure when to pick me up, so she's just gonna' stay and sit in the back of the church until it's over. I look back, and she's three rows behind me. And she sees me looking, and she kinda' gives me this little smile. It only lasts a second, but—you ever just sit in front of the window in the morning when the sun is coming in, like in a really comfortable chair? It's like that.

(*Pause.*)

The school select choir starts singing "Amazing Grace," and one of the kids can't make it through. And the director stops conducting and sits her down, but the choir keeps going. They start to rush the song, and I look back at my mom again, only this time she's watching the girl from the choir and not looking at me.

(*Pause.*)

And when "Amazing Grace" finishes and the captain of the soccer team gets up to recite Evan's stats and ask why somebody that just set the league scoring record could hang himself in a garage, I look back again. And she's watching the captain of the soccer team cry and not watching me. And in that second I miss her again, I want to— (*Beat.*) When I was little I used to ride the bus. And I talked to everybody. The person next to me—that was always my best friend, Ellen—the kids in the seat across from us, and in the row behind us and the row in front of us, and in the row behind them and the row ahead of them. No seat on the bus is too far to talk to. Three rows is nothing. But when you need your mom to be a nice warm seat in the morning sun, three rows in a church is infinity.

ZERO TOLERANCE

(A GIRL sits in a chair. The PRINCIPAL and a TEACHER and a POLICE OFFICER stand over her.)

GIRL: I didn't mean I was gonna' kill him.

POLICE OFFICER 1: Search her locker for guns, knives, bombs—

GIRL: It's an expression. I probably say it five times a day.

POLICE OFFICER 1: Molotov cocktails, Chinese throwing stars, grenades—

GIRL: I say it to my hamster when he doesn't want to get on the wheel.

PRINCIPAL: Young lady, saying "I'm gonna' kill you" is something we take very seriously at this school.

GIRL: It was a joke. *(To the Teacher:)* Couldn't you see I was kidding?

POLICE OFFICER 1: Blackjacks, needles, vials filled with biological weapons—

TEACHER: I heard the words "I'm gonna' kill you." I have to report that.

GIRL: Ask Todd—he knows I was kidding.

POLICE OFFICER 1: There is no Todd here. Todd is a thing of the past. Vials filled with chemical weapons, napalm, rocket launchers, tactical nuclear weapons—

GIRL: But if I said it to Todd and he knows I was kidding—

POLICE OFFICER 1: No Todd! No Todd!

PRINCIPAL: If a teacher hears the words "I'm gonna' kill you," "I'm going to kill you," "You're dead" or "You dead," the teacher must inform the principal. I in turn must inform the police.

POLICE OFFICER 1: ICBMs, F-16s, C-4 —

PRINCIPAL: We have a zero-tolerance policy for violence.

GIRL: I wasn't gonna' be violent.

POLICE OFFICER 1: Trenchcoats, dead animals, albums that play backward and conjure the devil —

GIRL: I didn't know. If I knew it was so bad, I wouldn't have said it.

(Enter POLICE OFFICER 2.)

POLICE OFFICER 2: We'll take her.

GIRL: But —

POLICE OFFICER 2: Come on, you homicidal missy.

PRINCIPAL: It's out of our hands.

(The Police Officers grab the Girl, who resists, and start dragging her off the stage.)

POLICE OFFICER 1: Dead letters, letter bombs, movies that bombed, bad haircuts —

POLICE OFFICER 2: You have the right to remain silent. Anything you say —

GIRL: I didn't know!

POLICE OFFICER 1: Bad hair days, big hair, hair loss treatments, hair extensions —

POLICE OFFICER 2: can be used against you in a court of law. You have the right to an attorney —

GIRL: I want my parents!

POLICE OFFICER 2: Miranda Miranda Miranda!

POLICE OFFICER 1: Static hair, electric hair —

PRINCIPAL: You're not in elementary school anymore.

POLICE OFFICER 1: Shock treatments. Shock therapy.

PRINCIPAL: Your parents can't save you anymore —

GIRL: I shouldn't even be here. I don't go here.

POLICE OFFICER 1: The electric chair!

GIRL: I'm in elementary school.

TEACHER: I hope you learn something from this experience.

GIRL: I'm six years old.

POLICE OFFICER 1: A firing squad.

GIRL: No — not six. Four. No — two.

(She begins to cry in an exaggerated baby "wah." The Police Officers and the Girl reach the exit.)

GIRL: I'm just a baby! I wanna' be a baby! Waaahhh!

*(Exit the actors as it becomes a news broadcast, **CHUCK INTERLUDE #6**. Enter the ANCHOR.)*

ANCHOR: Our top story once again is the search for Chuck. Still no sign, and authorities are rushing to get his face on a milk carton. Anyone with information on Chuck's whereabouts, you can dial this toll free hotline: 1-888-GO-CHUCK. *(Pause.)* Moms and dads, do you know where your Chuck is?

ADVENTURES IN BABYSITTING

(A TEEN BABYSITTER, either gender, babysits another member of the ensemble, who transforms into a crying BABY, perhaps with a simple costume piece.)

BABYSITTER: Come on—look at the funny face. Look at the funny face! Ha ha ha ha ha!

(More crying.)

Come on. *(Beat.)* You want the bottle again? You want the bottle?

BABY: *(Not sounding like a baby anymore:)* No I don't want the bottle.

BABYSITTER: I'm trying everything.

BABY: And you're pretty crap at it.

BABYSITTER: You're pretty crap at being a baby. *(Beat.)* Sorry. Please don't tell your parents I said that.

BABY: Relax. I'm like six months away from simple words.

BABYSITTER: So then...wait—I'm losing it.

BABY: Somebody is not the sharpest bulb in the tack box.

BABYSITTER: What?

BABY: You don't even hallucinate good metaphors.

BABYSITTER: At least I know the word "hallucinate."

BABY: Congratulations. You can fail the next vocab quiz with a 50 instead of a 45.

BABYSITTER: I'm trying—OK? I stay after for help class and I get peer tutored by that kid who's always smirking down his glasses. I do flashcards and study sheets and I even tried writing on my arm but then I just couldn't do it 'cause like my pencil starts saying things like "don't go over to the dark side," and when I barely tug at my shirt it comes in with "you disgust me." I think I'm totally going crazy.

BABY: Talking about it is good.

BABYSITTER: I'm talking to crazy stuff. I mean what's next? A rabbit?

(Enter a member of the ensemble with bunny ears attached: a giant RABBIT.)

RABBIT: The baby fell asleep.

(The Baby instantly falls asleep.)

BABYSITTER: I am so crazy.

RABBIT: You're really not.

BABYSITTER: I'm talking to a rabbit.

RABBIT: It's a totally natural reaction to stress.

BABYSITTER: How many 17-year-olds talk to their—I don't even know who I'm really talking to.

RABBIT: Well, duh. Yourself. *(Beat.)* That's a start—right?

BABYSITTER: If this is what I do now, what happens when I get older and I suck at everything except being crazy?

RABBIT: You're not a bad babysitter.

BABYSITTER: But—

RABBIT: Baby's changed, baby's fed, baby's asleep. *(Beat.)* You did OK.

BABYSITTER: I'm still talking to a rabbit.

RABBIT: Baby steps.

*(The lights dim on them. Beat. A PHONE RINGS once or twice and then reaches a RECORDING. We are in **CHUCK INTERLUDE #7**. As we listen to the recording, a tweet projects: @everybody Chuck, please come home. We miss you. We need you. #searchforchuck." In a lower tech production, this could be accomplished with cast members holding cardboard signs that together make up the tweet.)*

RECORDING: The number you have reached has been disconnected or is no longer in service. If you feel you have reached this recording in error —

BABEL, OR A CYBER SYMPHONY

(A BOY and a GIRL message back and forth on computers. These could be laptops, keyboards to imply computers, or even typing into the air. Their lines are typed, but the actors might also speak them, or they could be projected. The lack of punctuation at times is intentional, but if spoken, speak them conversationally.)

BOY: hey

GIRL: hey

(The sound of a text message arriving on the Girl's phone. Lights up on TEXTING GIRL.)

TEXTING GIRL: r we mallin it tonight?

BOY: how r u?

GIRL: *(Texting:)* not sure if i can *(Typing to the Boy:)* good u

BOY: good. so wassup

TEXTING GIRL: lame. i dont want 2 go alone with jeannie

GIRL: nothing u?

BOY: chillin

GIRL: *(Texting:)* sorry paper *(Typing to the Boy:)* cool

BOY: cool so...

TEXTING GIRL: so lame. i am gonna die

GIRL: shes not that bad

TEXTING GIRL: look at her instagram omg

(Various ACTORS enter and become "instruments" in a cyber symphony surrounding the Boy and the Girl.)

GIRL: *(Typing to the Boy:)* brb

(The actors and their lines in the following "cyber symphony" are meant to overlap. Another actor who doesn't speak should serve as CONDUCTOR.)

FIRST TECHNOBABBLER: LOL. LMAO. ROFL. ROFLMAO. BRB. TTYL. TTYS. B4N. BFF. CT. D/C. CYO. FBOCD. G2G. GN. h/o. J/K. HMU. ICW. IDC. IDK. IMHO. IMR. IONO. J/W. LTR. NMU. NP. PLO. PLZ. S2R. TMI. WE. OMG. XOXO. ILY.

SECOND TECHNOBABBLER: Do you like my new haircut? Comment on how much you like my haircut.
Me with my friends. Don't I have a lot of friends? Don't we look like we're having an awesome time?
Comment.
Pictures of my dog.
Pictures of me and my dog.
Aren't me and my dog awesome?
Comments on our awesomeness.
Pictures of a dog I don't even know.
Comment on how random I am.
Pictures of me standing behind some dude I don't even know.
Comment on how cool I am for being in this photo.
Me doing nothing.
Comment. Comment. Comment.

THIRD TECHNOBABBLER: Sign up for weekly offers from—
The cheetah is the world's fastest land mammal, reaching speeds of up to—
Teen celebrity of the month breaks leg in three-legged race. Watch the video.

Three sneakers for the price of two.
Random pop-up screen to win a—
Sign your name if you're angry about—
So you want to be an architect...?
Check the scores for all of today's games—
Today's forecast is partly cloudy with a chance of—

FOURTH TECHNOBABBLER: You've killed something really big.
You have advanced to the second level.
You have new ammunition.
You have advanced to the third level.
You've won new weapons.
You have advanced to the fourth level.
You have new soldiers.
You have a new army.
You've earned an extra life.
You have reached the fifth level.
You have achieved Nirvana-mageddon!

FIFTH TECHNOBABBLER: Like. Like. Like. Like. [etc]

(The Boy closes his computer and puts away his cell phone. Lights out on all of the Technobabblers. The Boy steps into the Girl's space.)

BOY: So...how are you?

GIRL: Good. You?

BOY: No—really. How are you doing?

(Beat. The Girl puts away all of her technological gadgets.)

GIRL: Well...

BOY: I'm listening.

(Lights dim on them.)

CHUCK INTERLUDE #8: DEAR CHUCK REPRISE

(Enter an ACTOR of either gender, not necessarily the same one who read the first letter. The Actor carries a letter and an envelope. This monologue could also be divided among several letter writers.)

ACTOR: Dear Chuck,

This will be my last letter, because none of the other ones seem to be reaching you, or if they are, you're not writing back. There's so much I want to say to you, so many questions I want to ask. I want to start by saying I'm sorry. I probably didn't mean half the things I said to you—I feel like I'm crazy most of the time, and half-crazy the rest of it.

(Pause.)

What's it like out there, Chuck? Maybe I should start by asking where "out there" is. Or what it is. Wherever and whatever "there" is, I wanna' get there soon. Or maybe I don't. Maybe I want to get there later. Is this what they mean by "sooner or later"?

(Pause.)

I was thinking maybe I should send you a list of things I want to know about. Things that—now that you're out there—you should know. Like do you laugh more or cry more? Is Santa Claus really not real, or is it all an elaborate cover-up he created so people would stop nagging him and keeping him from getting anything done? Same goes for the Easter Bunny, and do you talk to your parents the same way you did before? Who do people expect you to be, and who do you expect you to be? Should they be the same thing, or maybe the better question is where do you fit in the world of the people you know or the people you love, or the people you live with or work with or play with, or maybe I should ask how do you fit or make yourself fit, and what if you don't fit? What are you doing about all of these issues, Chuck? Please write.

Love,

(The Actor should say his or her first name here.)

p.s. If you come home, would I recognize you?

(The Actor seals the letter in the envelope and exits.)

FINALE: THE COMING OF CHUCK

(A BOY with war paint on his face builds a fort using blocks or whatever objects are on stage. Enter BOY 2.)

BOY: We've got them surrounded.

BOY 2: They've got reinforcements coming.

BOY: Help me build up the fort.

(They continue to construct a fort around themselves during the rest of the scene.)

How many reinforcements?

BOY 2: Aly and Kaya are the ones we've got surrounded, and Megan, Charlotte, Stephanie and I forget the other ones that are comin'.

BOY: Who's on our side?

BOY 2: Alec, Michael, Seth—I tried to get Sam, but he said he'd rather hang out with Nikita.

BOY: You told him I was playin'?

BOY 2: He said he didn't want to.

BOY: He played last week.

BOY 2: He said no.

BOY: Why's this week different from last week?

(Enter GIRLS 1 and 2.)

Whose side are you on?

GIRL 1: Yours.

GIRL 2: No — it's boys against girls.

GIRL 1: *(To Boy 1:)* I wanna' be on your team.

(Enter BOY 3, aka Sam, and GIRL 3, aka Nikita.)

BOY 2: I thought you weren't coming.

BOY 3: You're too old to be playing with forts.

GIRL 3: Sam and I have more mature things to do.

(Sam and Nikita start building a fort of their own. Enter GIRLS 4, 5 and 6. From this point on, cast members should enter as necessary until the stage is filled — except for one girl.)

GIRL 4: Forts are for kids.

(She joins Sam and Nikita's group. Newly arriving cast members should divide between the two groups.)

BOY 2: I'm only a year younger than you.

GIRL 5: You act like it's 10.

BOY 1: We're just having fun.

GIRL 6: What if Chuck built the fort? Would you play in it then?

GIRL 7: That would be different. If Chuck did it —

GIRL 8: Chuck doesn't play with forts.

GIRL 7: How do you know?

BOY 4: If Chuck did it, then it would be OK.

GIRL 9: Well, I guess if Chuck did it...

BOY 5: Why would Chuck play with forts?

GIRL 10: Chuck's too old for forts. All the things he knows, all the places he's been...Chuck's not a kid anymore.

GIRL 11: Maybe he just does it for a break. For fun.

GIRL 12: Chuck doesn't need fun.

GIRL 13: How do you know?

GIRL 12: I know Chuck.

BOY 6: Yeah right. And I know your mom.

GIRL 12: You do know my mom.

BOY 6: Oh yeah. *(Pause.)* But you still don't know Chuck.

BOY 7: What if he doesn't know what he needs?

(Everyone stops building.)

How do you know that Chuck knows what he needs?

GIRL 14: He's Chuck. He knows.

BOY 7: What if he doesn't?

GIRL 15: What are you saying?

BOY 7: I'm saying I don't know what I'm saying, and maybe Chuck doesn't either. Maybe he's like me.

BOY 8: Or me.

GIRL 16: Or me. Sometimes. Most of the time I know what I'm saying. I think.

(The fort construction resumes.)

BOY 9: Most of the time she's half nuts.

GIRL 17: Better than being all nuts like you.

GIRL 18: *(Gets into a tug-of-war over a block:)* Why are we fighting over what Chuck would do? He's not here, and he's not coming back — so we'll never know.

GIRL 19: I wish we did.

GIRL 20: I wish Chuck was here.

GIRL 21: Chuck would solve everything. He always did.

(*Enter GIRL 22.*)

GIRL 22: Chuck's back!

VARIOUS VOICES: He is?
Yes!
Where is he?
When's he coming?
When's he gonna' be here?

GIRL 22: He says he's not coming here.

BOY 1: Why not?

GIRL 1: How can he be back and not wanna' come here?

GIRL 22: He says we have to look for him.

BOY 1: But that's what we've been doing.

GIRL 22: He says we have to keep doing it.

GIRL 2: For how long?

BOY 2: Yeah—how much longer?

GIRL 22: He didn't say. All he said is keep looking, and we'll know him when we find him. Maybe. But not to worry.

BOY 3: Not to worry?

GIRL 22: Yeah. He said he's been there, and not to worry.

(*Beat. The lights slowly fade. End of play.*)

BRAN AND BANANAS

(This monologue may be substituted for THREE ROWS depending on the needs of your production. A TEEN of either gender holds a bowl of bran and bananas.)

TEEN: When I was like six, my dad had an awesome job. I don't actually know what he did, but he was home having breakfast when I was having breakfast for school. He'd have bran cereal every day. He said it kept him regular. I thought that meant if he didn't have it his head would spin around and he'd puke green slime or something, so I was glad for the bran. I didn't want that to happen to me either — and I figure my dad knows what he's doing so I have it too. Only can we add some honey to mine, 'cause not turning into a monster doesn't taste as good as I was hoping. And I wake up 15 minutes early, 'cause my dad's reading the newspaper, and he reads the sports with me. We do this every morning until I'm in middle school.

(Beat.)

Yeah, I know your parents aren't cool, but it's not like people can see us.

(Pause.)

In seventh grade, my dad switches to Greek yogurt and fruit, because it's protein and low carb, and he drinks coffee but not fruit juice. I stick to bran, but if Dad's doing fruit, I'm doing fruit. Mostly bananas. Mom cuts them up and leaves them in a bowl covered with wax paper. She spends breakfast taking showers — she says this is father-son time — but as long as the fruit's in the bowl and I can just dump it on the bran, life is good. And when we finish, Dad goes into his study and Mom comes out of the shower and I go to school.

(Beat.)

But it gets harder when he moves to the other side of town. So breakfast turns into brunch, which is something that happens on Saturdays and Sundays.

(*Beat.*)

And then Dad gets a job three states away. This time, I know he designs buildings, and brunch becomes summer. But this year, there's music and tennis and tutoring for my SATs because my mom is freaking out that they're going to be too low. I don't think she's doing it on purpose, but I think I can only see him for a week this year.

(*Beat.*)

I'm glad the screaming matches and the silences that made me want to get up and run away are over, but a week of breakfasts...? I know I shouldn't—I know it's better for everybody—but part of me would trade a few more broken coffee mugs and an earful of words that made the stuff kids say at school seem like hugs and kisses for a few more breakfasts of bran and bananas.

(*End of scene.*)

The Author Speaks

What inspired you to write this play?

Dear Chuck was originally a commission for Choate Rosemary Hall's Summer Arts Conservatory. A commission is one of those rare occasions where they actually pay you to write the play, rather than you writing it and hoping someone will pay you to produce it. The tricky part at Choate was that you were there five weeks, during which not only did I have to write much of the play—I think I wrote a little of it before I got there—but we had to put it up. I started by having discussions with the students, who ranged from middle school or even upper elementary to late high school (which is a tricky range to include all together in one play), and from there I wrote more scenes and monologues. New scenes would show up every day during rehearsal for several weeks until we finally had a coherent play. I even adapted a journal entry by Daniel Sobol, a wonderful and wonderfully talented young man (I think he was maybe 13 or 14 at the time) who later went on to graduate from Brown University, as a monologue for the play.

Was the structure of the play influenced by any other work?

The structure of *Dear Chuck* emerged out of my efforts to solve a problem: I had to write a play for 31 young actors, and to give everybody meaningful stage time. That is not an easy task. I didn't want to write a play with lots of people standing around, so after some conversations with the director and my colleagues, I arrived at the conclusion that the most realistic way to accomplish my goal was to create an episodic piece of related scenes and monologues. What's interesting is that while *Dear Chuck* may not have been influenced by other pieces, it actually influenced a number of my plays that came after it. You'll see that episodic, "collected scenes and monologues" style in *After Math, 4 A.M., The Magic Hour* and *Thank You for Flushing My Head in the Toilet and other rarely used expressions.* I like it because it allows me to experiment with different combinations of actors on stage at any given time, giving the play different looks throughout, from a single person to a large choral moment. Even plays that have a more traditional, linear story, like *The Locker Next 2 Mine, Rumors of Polar Bears, Just Add Zombies* and *Harry's Hotter at Twilight,* still make use of a similar episodic, almost cinematic structure.

Have you dealt with the same theme in other works that you have written?
Dear Chuck is very much a coming of age play. While I deal with a lot of themes that are pertinent to young people in my more serious plays for teens, and characters are constantly moving to a place of greater understanding (for example, the characters in *The Locker Next 2 Mine*), *Dear Chuck* is probably unique in my body of work in that it really focuses on that journey from childhood to adulthood. This isn't to say that particular characters aren't coming of age in other plays of mine. Romulus in *Rumors of Polar Bears* or Brady in *The Locker Next 2 Mine* or Frankie in *4 A.M.*, who moves from asking the question, "Is anybody out there?" to making a statement that "I know you're out there," are all on that journey.

What were the biggest challenges involved in the writing of this play?
At the time, the biggest challenge in writing *Dear Chuck* was the fact that I was writing much of it while we were literally in the middle of the rehearsal process. On top of that, I was working with the young playwrights at the conservatory, teaching them and dramaturging their projects, which would also get readings at the end of the summer, so I had to be extremely organized with my time. But it helped that the process of creating a new play with young actors who are all

right there with you every day is so exciting—I think the adrenaline rush helped get me through. Another challenge came later, after I successfully got the play back from its original publisher (that was a challenge in itself). I felt that it had dated a bit over the years, and I had to dive back into its world to rewrite old scenes and create new ones. I had the luck to meet a talented young director, Jonathan Muñoz-Proulx, rather randomly at this panel at the University of Southern California (he was a recent grad, and many of my friends teach there), and after that, we struck up a friendship. When I returned to the world of *Dear Chuck*, Jonathan helped me set up a pair of readings and was an excellent sounding board as I reworked the play.

What inspired you to become a playwright?
I've always enjoyed writing. I got my start writing short stories in elementary school. I used to read constantly—luckily, we didn't really have the distraction of the internet at that time. Fast forward to the end of tenth grade, when somehow I became the editor of the high school newspaper. The newspaper advisor was a teacher named Tom Williams. He was a great musician and a world-class poet. We became very close—in fact, he went on to become one of my best friends and collaborators. In addition to my newspaper writing, he encouraged me to write poetry and songs. I would often write lyrics and he'd musicalize them, and occasionally I'd plunk out a melody myself on a synth I'd bought. But Tom had also written plays, and during my junior year, he told me that I'd written everything else—why not try writing a play? So I did. It was a one-act called *The Storm*. Looking back on it, it was probably a bad Eugene O'Neill rip-off (is there a good Eugene O'Neill rip-off?), but people seemed to like it at the time, and Tom encouraged one of the seniors in the drama program to direct it in the year-end one-act festival. It was supposedly the

first student-written play produced at my high school. The next year I wrote another one — *Death Without Parole*, which was a bad Eugene Ionesco rip-off. Not only did it get produced in that year's festival, but I even played a small role. I remember being terrified that the other actor in the scene would forget his lines, and I think he actually did, but I managed to cover. And eventually I wrote better plays.

How did you research the subject?
There wasn't "research" in the traditional look it up in the library sense, but rather the play evolved out of my own experiences (both as a student and as a teacher of middle and high school students) and those of the students of the Choate Rosemary Hall Summer Arts Conservatory, with whom I had several days of discussions (as well as weeks of rehearsal). Later, when I revisited the play, I was working with college-age actors, who were close enough to their high school days to bring a new set of relevant experiences to inform the world I was creating. And truth be told, I did make one foray into the world of "research." For the scene entitled "Babel, or A Cyber Symphony," I spent time researching internet slang. It blew my mind to discover that there are literally thousands of cyber shorthand expressions out there beyond the most common ones that we all know (e.g. BRB, ROFL, etc.).

How was the first production different from the vision that you created in your mind?
I was integrally involved in the development and rehearsal of the play at Choate, so I can't say I was terribly surprised by what ended up on stage. At the same time, no play *ever* makes it from my brain to the stage unscathed. It's what I love so much about the theatre. Sure, I love the little productions that take place in my head while I'm writing, but I truly love what I talented cast (of any age) and a passionate production team can bring to a show. Inevitably something (or more than one

something) isn't exactly the way I would have done it, but I accept that, and I look forward to the awesome surprises that collaboration can bring.

About the Author

Jonathan Dorf is a Los Angeles-based playwright, screenwriter, teacher and script consultant, whose plays have been produced in every state in the US, as well as in Canada, Europe, Asia, Africa, Australia and New Zealand. He is Co-Chair of the Alliance of Los Angeles Playwrights and the Resident Playwriting Expert for Final Draft and The Writers Store. He directed the theatre program at The Haverford School and spent three years at Choate Rosemary Hall Summer Arts Conservatory as playwright-in-residence. He is a frequent guest artist at Thespian conferences and schools, and has served as Visiting Professor in the MFA Playwriting and Children's Literature programs at Hollins University, and as United States cultural envoy to Barbados. He is the author of *Young Playwrights 101*, a playwriting textbook, and of Playwriting101.com, for years Google's top-ranked playwriting website. He holds a BA in Dramatic Writing and Literature from Harvard College and an MFA in Playwriting from UCLA. His website is http://jonathandorf.com.

About YouthPLAYS

YouthPLAYS (www.youthplays.com) is a publisher of award-winning professional dramatists and talented new discoveries, each with an original theatrical voice, and all dedicated to expanding the vocabulary of theatre for young actors and audiences. On our website you'll find one-act and full-length plays and musicals for teen and pre-teen (and even college) actors, as well as duets and monologues for competition. Many of our authors' works have been widely produced at high schools and middle schools, youth theatres and other TYA companies, both amateur and professional, as well as at elementary schools, camps, churches and other institutions serving young audiences and/or actors worldwide. Most are intended for performance by young people, while some are intended for adult actors performing for young audiences.

YouthPLAYS was co-founded by professional playwrights Jonathan Dorf and Ed Shockley. It began merely as an additional outlet to market their own works, which included a substantial body of award-winning published and unpublished plays and musicals. Those interested in their published plays were directed to the respective publishers' websites, and unpublished plays were made available in electronic form. But when they saw the desperate need for material for young actors and audiences—coupled with their experience that numerous quality plays for young people weren't finding a home—they made the decision to represent the work of other playwrights as well. Dozens and dozens of authors are now members of the YouthPLAYS family, with scripts available both electronically and in traditional acting editions. We continue to grow as we look for exciting and challenging plays and musicals for young actors and audiences.

About ProduceaPlay.com

Let's put up a play! Great idea! But producing a play takes time, energy and knowledge. While finding the necessary time and energy is up to you, ProduceaPlay.com is a website designed to assist you with that third element: knowledge.

Created by YouthPLAYS' co-founders, Jonathan Dorf and Ed Shockley, ProduceaPlay.com serves as a resource for producers at all levels as it addresses the many facets of production. As Dorf and Shockley speak from their years of experience (as playwrights, producers, directors and more), they are joined by a group of award-winning theatre professionals and experienced teachers from the world of academic theatre, all making their expertise available for free in the hope of helping this and future generations of producers, whether it's at the school or university level, or in community or professional theatres.

The site is organized into a series of major topics, each of which has its own page that delves into the subject in detail, offering suggestions and links for further information. For example, Publicity covers everything from Publicizing Auditions to How to Use Social Media to Posters to whether it's worth hiring a publicist. Casting details Where to Find the Actors, How to Evaluate a Resume, Callbacks and even Dealing with Problem Actors. You'll find guidance on your Production Timeline, The Theater Space, Picking a Play, Budget, Contracts, Rehearsing the Play, The Program, House Management, Backstage, and many other important subjects.

The site is constantly under construction, so visit often for the latest insights on play producing, and let it help make your play production dreams a reality.

More from YouthPLAYS

Rumors of Polar Bears by Jonathan Dorf
Dramedy. 90-100 minutes. 8-25+ females, 4-15+ males (14-40+ performers possible).

A ragtag band of teens hits the road to survive a climate induced catastrophe. As they encounter unfinished coloring books and failing paradises, a frozen-in-time former pre-kindergarten drama class, bikers determined to turn the chaos into their new world order, and a mysterious people that even the bikers won't cross, will the refugees follow Deme and chase after the rumored polar bears that she believes are the key to their survival, or will their patchwork family fall apart?

Les Examables by Don Zolidis
Comedy. 100-110 minutes. 8-28 females, 5-25 males (15-40+ performers possible).

Tired of too much standardized testing in her high school, high achiever Anna Ullman stages a protest and finds herself crowned the new principal. But ultimate power comes with its own problems (especially after death threats from the all-powerful State Board of Ed), and soon Anna descends into madness, imposing even more standardized testing. It's up to her former best friend, Lola, to bring down this new tyrant. Soon Lola is manning the barricades and singing triumphantly awesome songs in this insane satire based on the mega-musical *Les Misérables*.

Clay by Carol S. Lashof
Dramedy. 30-40 minutes. 2 males, 2 females.

Aaron, Zeta and Will are as different as three students could be. One works tirelessly yet struggles to pass. One excels by cutting every corner, and one attends school intermittently despite exceptional intelligence and creativity. Forced to interact by a group assignment, they confront themselves, each other and the magic of molding clay.

Prime by Ellen Margolis
Comedy. 80-85 minutes. 6 females, 6 males, 6 either.

Princess Dar and Prince Dion, young royals from neighboring kingdoms, are destined for each other through an arranged marriage. On the eve of the wedding, however, they decide to run away and discover their own futures. Escaping to a nearby valley, they cross paths with disoriented lovers, hot-headed party animals, desperate draft dodgers, and a number-obsessed hermit. Identities are investigated, resources stretched, and every kind of love put to the test.

ShakeSPLOSION!!! by Andrew Geha
Comedy. 75-85 minutes. 9-21+ females, 4-14+ males (14-100+ performers possible).

ShakeSPLOSION!!! is a madcap sprint through every play written by the Bard. From 235 years of English kings in the History Plays, to (nearly) every bloody death in the Tragedies, to every girl who dressed up as a boy in the Comedies, it's like watching Shakespeare's entire canon fired out of a cannon—scattering prose, verse and characters across the stage. Sword fights! Word fights! Witches, ghosts and murder! All in 80 minutes!! Performed by teenagers!!!

Warriors by Hayley Lawson-Smith
Drama. 40-50 minutes. 4 females, 1 male.

Not every hero gets a song or the cheers of the crowd—or even acknowledgement. In Zordana's land, a hero fights bravely in the open field, destroying monsters and dark magic. In Amy's world, her hero is the sister who takes care of her. For Maddie, her hero is her brother, who may tease her mercilessly but loves her dearly. As tragedy threatens to consume their separate worlds, only in coming together can they battle back the dark.